Lancashire
this, that an' t'other

LANCASHIRE
This, That an' t'Other

Poems & Stories
Written & Illustrated
by

Doris Snape

Landy Publishing
1997

Copyright in the material in this book is claimed by Doris Snape

British Library Cataloguing in Publication Data. A catalogue record of this book is available from the British Library.

ISBN 1 872895 37 9

Layout by Mike Clarke, Tel & Fax: 01254 395848

Printed by Nayler The Printer Ltd. Tel: 01254 234247

Landy Publishing have also published:
Threads of Lancashire Life by Winnie Bridges
A Lancashire Look by Benita Moore
An Accrington Mixture by Bob Dobson
Accrington Observed by Brian Brindle & Bob Dobson
Accrington's Changing Face by Frank Watson & Bob Dobson
Blackburn's West End by Matthew Cole
Blackburn's Shops at the Turn of the Century by Matthew Cole
A Blackburn Miscellany edited by Bob Dobson

A full list of books is available from:
Landy Publishing, 'Acorns' 3 Staining Rise, Staining, Blackpool FY3 0BU

Preface

This is a collection of verse and short stories in both Lancashire dialect and Standard English. Whilst many people are still able to speak and understand local dialect, a great many find it difficult to read. It is with this thought in mind that I chose to combine the two differing styles in the hope that the book will reach a wider public, and also that I might make one or two converts either way.

My poems and stories seemed to fall naturally into four groups:= Early Days, my own and those of my children and grandchildren; People, mostly real with a little embroidery added; Places; and Age, about which, having attained three score and ten, I feel I can write with convictions and authority.

I would like to thank Bob Dobson for his patience, though this may come as a shock to his family; and extend my thanks to Lorna Snape and Christine Cunliffe for their help in preparation.

I dedicate this book to the memory of Steve Hezzlewood, a multi-talented man who, before his premature death, had promised to illustrate my book. I have used one of his drawings to illustrate 'When Ah wor a lass' and 'Mi grandad'.

Doris Snape
Great Harwood
August 1997

Contents.

Mi Grandad

Mi Grandad 'ad a gardin
Next to t'other fooakses' pens.
He'd raspberries an' tomaytas,
But they'd nobbut ducks an' 'ens.

Mi Grandad 'ad a green'eawse
Wur 'e'd sit an' smooak fer 'eawrs,
An' when Ah set theer wi' 'im
'E'd tell mi aw abeawt fleawrs.

Mi Grandad towd mi t'fairies
Lived at t'back of 'is green'eawse,
An'eaw thi lived o'dew drops
An rooad a lickle meawse.

An' then one day mi Grandad,
'E jus' wouldn'd wakken up,
Mi Gran'ma sed as t'fairies
'Ad bin wi' a silver cup.

Oo sed as eaw mi Grandad's een
Wor filled wi' fairy dust.
Ah went sthraight deawn to t'green'eawse
An' them fairies worn'd aif cussed!

Ah towd 'em as mi Grandad
'Ad belonged to me, nod them,
An' then Ah started scrykin',
An' Ah've ne'er liked fairies sin'.

The Green Eye of the Little Yellow Girl

Ah 'ate Cissy Braithwaite in eawr class.
Oo's a lass as Ah really carned stand;
Wi' 'er reyt snooty voice an' posh clooathes,
An' oo lives in a 'eawse that's reyt grand.

When oo fost came Ah thried ta like 'er,
So Ah thowt as Ah'd tell 'er mi name,
Ah smiled an' sed "Ah'm Mary Wikkiter."
An' oo stared an' sed "Oh, what a shame!"

Ee, things like thad fair mek mi blood boil;
An' Ah'm nod tekkin thad from no toff;
So Ah glared an' sed, "Miss 'Ighanmighty,
An which muck-cart es ta tumbled off?"

Aw t'lads in eawr class used ta like me.
Neaw thi' aw buzz reawnd 'er jus like flies
When oo pouts 'er pink lips, 'n oo simpers,
An' then flutters 'er puppy-dog eyes.

Oo allus comes top at exam time;
An' guess why - because oo's teycher's pet:
Bud if 'er dad warned one o't'governors
Oo'd be nearer ta t'bottom Ah bet.

Oo's really ruined wi' presents,
An' oo swanks abeawt aw thad who gets;
Cos when Ah geet a kitten fer Christmas
Cooarse a pony joined rest of 'er pets.

Las' summer we'd three days at Blackpoo'
Bud where oo went give aw't'class a shock;
"We'd two weeks with mummy in Disneyland,
Then met daddy and flew to Bangkok."

Id meks mi fair sick when oo's braggin'.
'Onestly Ah dorned think as it's fer,
As some folk should be rich, an' some poor.
Ah jus' wish oo wur me.........an' me 'er!

"Looking Through the Window"

When I was a child we were not poor, but neither were we rich, unless you count non-monetary riches; in which case, our family were millionaires.

We teetered on the tightrope of poverty, as my mother's cherished possessions, including her wedding ring and Grandma's vases moved to and from the local pawnshop with unfailing regularity. My mother's running battle with poverty was entirely due to an accumulation of medical bills, and it was her indomitable spirit and amazing capacity for physical hard labour that always ensured that our family of six remained, however closely, on the right side of respectability.

Like many other Lancashire families, the financial climate of the twenties and thirties, forced us to take our pleasures simply. My greatest delight was to sit at the front bedroom window with my eldest sister and watch the world go by.

After a fall down a long flight of stone steps when she was twelve, Edith never grew again, except outwards, and as she had damaged her skull, this too had grown to a rather peculiar shape. Now at twenty, she never joined in the Sunday afternoon parades and though Mother made her pretty dresses, Edith was often the target for cruel jibes; so on Sunday she stayed in.

Usually, I would rush home from afternoon Sunday School and charge upstairs with a cushion, then spend the rest of the day until teatime, looking through the window with Edith. Besides watching people, Edith told me stories and taught me to read.

But on one special day of the year we would spend the whole day there and I was even allowed to miss Sunday School. On the first Sunday in May the spectacle began in the early morning as the local milkmen did their rounds. Three milk floats passed our house and all of them kept their May Day decorations on until the first Monday after. The carts, one of which was beautifully painted in chestnut-brown and decorated with red, green and gold, were polished until the sides and shafts reflected the sunshine, which always seemed present on this wonderful day. The milk churns shone like silver and the brass handles on their lids like burnished gold.

But it was the horses I liked best. Their coats were groomed and shining, accentuating their firm, rippling muscles; their manes sleekly plaited with ribbons, or brushed into beautiful soft cascades and beribboned at the top only. For me, Cleopatra visiting Caesar could not have been more resplendent.

For the events of the day, our house was perfectly positioned, overlooking the main road where it crossed the stream, and set back slightly from the road; to the left was township of Oswaldtwistle and to the right Stanhill village.

This was the day that the Stanhill Methodists walked, and as many of them were relatively wealthy, many people with aspirations to grandeur turned out in their latest finery to pay homage, whilst the more humble simply went along to watch the procession.

The fashion parade began about nine o'clock and was livened by the local brass band, marching to the school, smartly turned out in blue uniforms trimmed with red and gold, playing gustily on their lovingly polished instruments, their calloused hands camouflaged by white cotton gloves.

At ten o'clock the procession left the school, winding its way down Stanhill Lane, past our house until it reached the Black Dog. There it halted and whilst the banner bearers battled with the ever present breeze, a short defiant service was held on the inn's cobbled forecourt. Then after a couple of hymns, a reading and a few words from their hell-fire minister; the procession would regroup and return to the school, banners flying and the band blasting out well-worn hymns.

As they passed us for a second time it was plain to see that more than one member of the Mother's class, who brought up the rear, were beginning to regret the smart new shoes, which had been their pride and joy on the outward journey.

With the exception of the Baptists, to whom we belonged, most schools and churches walked in those days, but Stanhill's peculiar blend of religion and nepotism gave it originality.

Every year the two daughters of the congregation's most affluent member led the procession, and he had good reason to be proud. Invariably they wore white satin dresses and white silk shoes, their lovely dark hair was loosely dressed and tied with a broad satin ribbon, but they were not only beautiful. As these visions of privilege walked along, no doubt paying more homage to self-importance than to religion, they played stirring hymns on their violins.

The stewards came next in hierarchical glory, and it was their daughters who held the ribbons controlling the groups of tiny children, who fanned out across the road like sweet peas in their pretty pastel coloured dresses.

The only acknowledgement of another stratum of society was in the choice of banner bearers, when muscle was given precedence over money. After all the deacons were needed to walk beside the mayor, and they couldn't possibly entertain him afterwards if they were sweating with the effort of controlling their beautiful new banner one of the largest in Oswaldtwistle.

If the organisers dined well when the procession was ended, we stayed to watch the last of the visitors cross the bridge, and after tea, sat at the front door. Whilst our mothers discussed the day's hats, we children processed, dressed in adults' cast-off shoes and bits of old lace curtain and carrying banners made from old table cloths tied onto brush handles. Those days are far off, and today processions of witness seldom take place in Lancashire; and what was a source of delight to me then, I now see for what it was and I feel anger. Anger at the cruelty and ridicule my sister had to bear. Edith was a lovely person and deserved better than having to watch life go by...through the window.

'Ere's Lookin' Ad Thi

Ah 'ed such a nasty shock t'other neet,
Id wor summat Ah'd ne'er sin afoor,
Ah tell thi, id gi' mi such a freet
Ah nearly run reyt eawt thro' t'door.

Ah'd gone ta mi Uncle Lawrence's 'eawse,
'E wor a sowdjer i't'second warld war.
Ah'd 'ed mi tay, a plate o'lobsceawse,
Then sat waitin' for wod Ah'd gone for.

Mi uncle 'ud allus tell me as 'eaw
'E'd bin shipped 'ooam an 'orrable mess,
'E'd stood on a mine an' 'e wor neaw
Left wi one eye an' six fingers less.

When 'e towd me eaw thad mine 'ed blown up
'E did 'is best ta thry an' mek mi jump,
Bud Ah liked id best when 'e shut up
An' then screwed off 'is 'and from 'is stump.

Tha sis, 'e'd aw sooarts o'things to screw on,
Things fer cuttin', an' fer geddin' to grips
Wi knobs an' things, an' 'e'd even one
'E could use jus' fer stabbin' 'is chips.

Bud thad neet when 'e'd tekken eawt 'is case
Wi aw th'ooks in, as Ah've towd thee abeawt,
'E pud 'is two fingers up to 'is face
An' 'e then popped 'is left eye reyt eawt.

Then puddin' thad eye onto t'mantleshelf
'E bent deawn close an' whispered to me,
"While Ah'm nod 'ere thee be'ave thisel'
'Cos' yon eye theer'll keep watchin' thee."

Ah sat theer fer ages, frozzen to t'wick,
While thad eye looked deawn, unblinkin'ad me
Until 'e geet back, when uncle said, "Dick,
Tha daft thing, yon glass eye theer connad see."

When Ah geet 'ooam thad neet Ah towd mi dad,
Who shook 'is 'ead an' said, "Silly owd foo.
If 'e thries freetenin' thee ageean lad,
Why then, just thee tarn a blind eye too".

'It 'Im Ageean

Ah wor weshin' up i't'kitchen last neet
Wi't'sink full o'sooapy watter,
When t'dooar bustin' oppen gi' mi such a freet
Ah sheawted, "Good 'eavens! What's matter?"
Eawr Bert stood theer, 'is fore'ead aw red,
'Is face covered i' sluch snot an' dust,
"Ee Albert, what's 'appened ta thee?" Ah said,
An' stop skrykin' like thad, or tha'll bust.
Dorn'd say tha's bin fawin' deawn ageean?"
"Nay, Ah 'avened, Eawr Ethel." 'e said.
"Tha knows big Billy 'as lives at sixteen,
Well 'e's pushed mi, an' Ah've banged mi o'ead."
At thad Ah wasted no time i'chatter,
"Come wi me," Ah said "Albert mi lad,
There's a seyin' bloods thicker ner watter,
E's nod geddin' away wi' thad."
Eawtside i't'sthreet, Billy wor standin' theer,
"Thee come 'ere Bully Walker." Ah said.
"Tha 'itted eawr Albert when Ah worned 'ere.
'It 'im neaw, while Ah'm 'ere," Ah said.
'E looked, an' 'e grinned, an' 'it eawr Albert i't'gob
"Jus' thee thry thad once mooar," Ah yelled.
When 'e did, eawr Albert started ta sob
An' went deawn like a tree thad wor felled.
So Ah 'issed, "Jus' thee thry thad once mooar,"
Cos' bi then Ah wor geddin' reyt mad,
So 'e kicked eawr Albert lyin' o't'flooar,
Ee, Ah didn'd 'aif feel sorry fer t'lad.
Tho' t'poor thing 'ed a busted nooase
T'bully threatened 'im wor 'e wor laid,
So Ah picked eawr Albert up wi' is clooase,
"Come on 'ooam, or 'e'll kill thi!" Ah said.

T' Fost Kiss

Well...Ah couldn'd reytly say as thad kiss wor t'fost that Ah'd 'ed,
Mi mam an' mi dad 'ave kissed mi fer years when they've tucked mi up inta bed;
An' mi Uncle Jim near' gi'es mi a bath, every time 'e puckers 'is lips,
While mi gran tastes o' salt an' vinegar, 'cos oo loves eytin' fish 'n' chips.

Mi Uncle Bob sups whisky an' 'is smackers fair mek mi drunk,
An' if eawr Annie kisses mi cheek, Ah've black lip marks, becos oo's a punk.
Kissin' Aunt Dorothy' wi' 'er moustache is like kissin' a big fur rug,
An' mi grandad fair teks mi breath away, 'cos 'e wraps 'is up in an 'ug.

So tha sis wi' aw my relations Ah'm used ta bein' kissed,
It's jus' that 'til las' neet i't'pictures there wur summat Ah felt thad Ah'd missed.
'Cos aw mi pals 'ave bin braggin' fer years abeawt geddin' kisses fro lads;
While th'ony chaps' kisses Ah've tasted, wor mi grandad's, mi uncles 'n'dad's.

It's nod fer t'want o'bein' asked. Ah could o' bin kissed afoor,
Bud Ah fancied a kiss fro' Sean Connery, beside 'im t'rest seem poor. Well...t'lads
in eawr class are an 'orrable lot, wi voices aw cracked, an' spots, An' t'sixth
formers are aw big eaded, or else never goo eawt 'cos they're swots.

Bud las' neet deawn at th' 'Ippodrome, Ah met this good lookin' lad,
So, when 'e asked could 'e tek mi 'oom, Ah said ay, thinkin' this one's nod bad;
Then when wi getten ta t'dooar step an' 'e asked could 'e gi' mi a kiss.
Ah shut mi eyes an' prepared missel', thinkin' this lot wor too good ta miss.

Well...talk abeawt disappointin'! Ah tell thi id warn'd woth t'wait;
Mi owd Aunty Gertrude wi' thin, mean dry lips is ten times as passionate!
So, Ah think kissin' lads is nod fer me yet, an' taneet Ah'm stoppin' in,
'Cos neaw wi'is stubble scrattin' mi face, Ah've spots comin' all o'er mi chin.

When Ah Wor a Lass

"Con Ah 'ev telly on Gran'ma?" Ah said.
"Now, tha carned" oo said sharpish, "thi Grandad's i' bed."
"Bud Gran'ma" Ah said, "Ah've geet nowt to do,
"Ah've nobody ta play wi' when Ah'm off schoo'."

"When Ah wor thy age, abeawt six or seven,
Ah'd a' thowt nowt to do wor' aif way to 'eaven,
Yo kids o' today dorned know thad yer born
So shuddup thi' moitherin', it's schoo'day tomorn."

"Bud Gran'ma, Ah'm bored, Ah want to play eawt".
"Bored! thee! at thy age! wot ti talkin' abeawt,
Dorned use silly words like thad, why Good Lord,
When Ah wor a lass Ah'd no time to bi bored."

"Wod games did ta play when tha' wor a kid?
Tell mi, then 'appen Ah con do wod tha' did."
"Wi played tig, an' marbles an' 'opscotch an'aw,
An' skippin', an'aw sooarts o' games wi' a baw."

"Tig's na good wi'eawt nobody to chase,
An' Ah marned drop mi marbles all o'er place,
An' when Ah played 'opscotch tha smacked me on t'bum
An' said chalkin'on t'flags med t'place like a slum,

An' when Ah played skippin' tha fotched me in,
'Cos Ah tripped Mary Mills up, an oo's thad thin
Oo brokken booath wrists, an' thad warn'd aw,
'Er mam said Ah'd brokken their winda wi t'baw.

So Gran'ma tha sis, there's nowt Ah con play,
An' mi mam says Ah've getten to stop in today."
"Aw, gi mi some peace, an' put t'telly on,
Thi Grandad's up neaw, and my patience is gone."

Eawr Elsie's Eighteenth Do

Eawr Elsie wanted a party, last week when oo were eighteen.
So mi mam said, "Present or party, tha meks thi mind up between."
"A party," grinned eawr Elsie, "An' then ah can ask aw mi friends."
"But aw t'fam'ly comes too," mi mam said, "Or theer tha'll find t'matter ends."

At that eawr Elsie looked mad, an' said, "O! mam, but that's not fair;
Eaw can Ah try to impress mi pals if dad an' 'eawr Albert's there?"
Mi mam breathed 'eavy an' firmly said, "No fam'ly, then no do."
"Ah don't mind mi dad," wailed Elsie, "but why mun eawr Albert come too?"

"'E 'as to come," mi mam said, "We carned put 'im eawtside for t'neet.
Look luv, dorned thee fret thisel', Ah'll mek sure 'e doesn'd get under t'feet."
So Elsie 'ad to give in, but muttered under 'er breath,
"If 'e does owt as 'e shouldn'd, Ah'll choke t'little 'orror to death."

And so o't'neet o't'party, 'e were put ta oppenin' t'dooar;
'E did fine for fost ten minutes, then 'e dropped 'is marbles o't'flooar.
Next few minutes were chaos, as one after t'other fell in.
Tha couldn'd si t'flooar for bodies nor 'ear thisel' think for t'din.

One lass brokken 'er shoe 'eel, an' one fellah geet punsed i' th'eye;
An' when mi mam boxed eawr Albert's ears, eawr Elsie started to cry.
"Send 'im to bed mam," oo pleaded. But skrykin' were aw in vain.
Mi mam said oo'd think abeawt id, if 'e did owt silly again.

For next 'aif 'our, aw went well, 'til Mabel stood next to t'cheear;
Then t'screams oo let eawt were leawder, nor t'klaxon o'th'end o't'pier.
'Is meawse 'ad escaped from 'is pocket, an' crawled reyt up 'er skirt;
So oo slapped lad's face, as were t'nearest, an' called 'im a cheeky flirt.

Bud nobody listened to 'er, 'cos Albert 'ad just bin sick,
An' t'lass whose feet 'e'd bin sick on, were tekkin' er shoes off reyt quick.
Id wor then mi mam decided to send eawr Albert to bed.
Mi dad jumped at t'chance to tek 'im, 'cos t'music were splittin' 'is 'ead.

After that t'party settled deawn, an' Elsie started to smile,
Wi' booath 'er tormentors missin', oo felt 'appy for a while.
Oo set 'er cap at David a lad as oo'd fancied for years,
An' later while t'rest wor dancin' they wor kissin' under t'steers.

When t'others 'ad aw gone 'ooam, oo walked wi'im deawn to 't'gate,
Then mi dad stuck 'is 'eyd through t'windwa', an' sheawted, "Dorned be late!"
Elsie were frothin' when oo come back, an' threw 'ersel' deawn in t'cheear,
"Parties!" oo said, "They can keep 'em. Ah'm 'avin' a present next year!"

A Summer Afternoon

The horsehair stuffing in the sofa began to prick her legs. As quietly as she could the little girl inched them forwards, hoping that her dress would make the prickling stop, but it didn't. She had been sitting as still as she could for what seemed like the whole afternoon and her little plump legs felt sore through her thin summer dress.

Tears of self-pity pricked her eyes as she thought of the lovely sunshine outside the stuffy parlour, with its peeling brown wallpaper, heavy furniture and gloomy dark-green chenille curtains. Only one thing was interesting and that was the huge grandfather-clock in the corner, but she could only see it if she twisted her neck round. The clock had a shiny brass face, with a cheerful golden sun painted on it at one side, and a faded -yellowish sleepy moon on the other. When the big finger was at the top the clock made a beautiful deep noise, like Uncle Frank's cello when he played the music that made her mother cry.

The child sighed deeply, the only sound she had made since her mother had deposited her on the sofa and told her to be very quiet and sit still until she returned.

The clock chimed sonorously. Once more she screwed her little neck round, waited until the sound had faded, then turned her attention back to the window. It was impossible to see the garden through the thick white lace that covered the lower-half of the tall sash-window. The last time the clock had struck, the June sunshine had defeated the curtain and struggled past the large shiny brown pot on the dusty window-sill and the enormous glossy aspidistra. The leaves of this monster plant looked like thick green swords, trying to stop the cheeky sunshine from touching the glass dome on the mahogany sideboard. Underneath the glass was a brown speckled bird, surrounded by faded flowers and grasses.

The child felt sorry for the bird, which, like herself, was trapped in this dark room, and she had looked down at the pretty pink rosebuds on her dress and wondered if they would have turned brown before her mother would take her out into the sunshine again.

Now, however, the sun had given up its unequal battle with the curtains and the aspidistra and had moved on, leaving the sideboard and all its treasures to become one large shadowy shape in the corner.

She wished her mother would come. In all the time she had been waiting the inner door had only opened once. Then, her aunty had come out; taken a white, lace-trimmed handkerchief from a drawer, dabbed her eyes and without speaking had back gone into the other room, closing the door quietly behind herself as if she were going into church,

The little girl was puzzled.

Her mother and aunt couldn't be quarrelling, because she couldn't hear their voices, and when mother quarrelled she always raised her voice. Some nights, lying awake, the child could hear her parents shouting at each other and she would press her face into her pillow and cry herself to sleep.

Now she felt very cross with her mother and thought about how she had been enjoying herself that morning when she had been called in to dinner. She had been playing at shop in next door's backyard and had just finished making mud pies on some flat stones, decorating them with flower heads, and her friend had made some fat ice cream wafers with mud and big lilac leaves from the large old tree. The tree dominated the small yard, but within the outer branches was a secret cavern, the floor trampled flat, the roof, sweetly scented.

She remembered how she had run into the kitchen and eaten all her dinner, even though she hated cabbage, and the tapioca pudding which made her feel as if she was being sick going down instead of coming up. But today she didn't mind, because her mother said they were going to Aunt Nellie's farm.

Walking through the fields in the warm sunshine she had felt very happy. She had picked an armful of golden buttercups and delicate mauve mayflowers and even some bluebells from the other side of the ditch. Usually her mother stopped her from crossing on the stepping stones, but today she had walked along without speaking to her chattering daughter and had ignored the child's squeals of delight when the stones squelched and sucked as she crossed the brown watery channel.

It had been so lovely, but now...

Suddenly the little girl stiffened in horror. Maybe her mother didn't love her any more and had gone out through the front door and was never coming back to move her from this itchy sofa. Somebody must have put the bird on the sideboard and told it not to move, then when they found that it had died, they put some flowers round it and a glass case over the top. Maybe they would find her sitting on the sofa tomorrow and put a glass case over her.

Slowly she slid from her seat, tiptoed over to the bird which stared with beady eyes towards the fireplace with its faded family photographs. Holding the ornate beading on the sideboard with her little fat fingers, she strained upwards in order to see the bird better and was surprised to see her own face surrounded by flowers, looking back at her; gravely she studied her reflection, that is what I would look like she thought.

Then she heard a familiar noise, It was the cows being taken through the cobbled yard to the shippon, she couldn't see them through the window but she knew that Uncle Dick would be there behind them, keeping them from the garden with his birch stick.

She smiled, everything would be all right now. He would come in any minute, take off his old greasy flat cap, put her on his shoulders and take her down to the shippon where old Joe was milking, then he would set her down and, with a billy-can lid, he would scoop some of the warm frothy milk from the bucket and pass it to her. She licked her lips in anticipation and was about to climb back onto the sofa when the inner door opened and the two women emerged with swollen red faces.

Her mother kissed her aunt, then hugged her for a long time; then taking the child's hand said in a funny, shaky voice, "Come on love."

They walked out of the parlour, through the cheerful kitchen with its shiny pans and big white sink, past the long well scrubbed wooden table, where her bunch of flowers lay withering and out into the sun-baked yard.

She broke away from her mother and ran across the cobbles calling, "Uncle Dick! Uncle Dick!…but it was old Joe, he gave her a funny look, then followed the last of the sweet-smelling cows, with milk dripping from its swollen udders into the shippon.

"Come here," said her mother gently. She bent down and whispered, "We shan't be seeing Uncle Dick again, so don't mention his name when Aunt Nellie's near, there's a good girl."

The child was about to ask why, but as she looked up she saw tears glistening, so she squeezed her mother's hand tightly as they walked back through the fields in silence.

She had no need to ask, she knew why she mustn't mention his name. Two days before she had heard a neighbour talking about her daughter, who had gone very fat and run away. The mother, unaware of the two children in the lilac tree, had said, "I never want to hear her name mentioned again."

The little girl felt very sad, she had lots of aunts and uncles, but Uncle Dick was her favourite. Now he had run away.

Probably on his new motor-bike.

Last time they had visited the farm he had given her a ride round the bumpy yard, and her mother had laughed and shrieked,

"Take her off Richard! Kill yourself with that contraption if you want, but not my sweetie-pie."

The child looked up again at her mother, whose tears were now running freely down her cheeks, as she too was remembering their last visit and her prophetic, ill-chosen words.

In her mind's eye she saw him again, a noisy tousle-haired child, her loveable younger brother, from whom the sun seemed to shine on everyone. How tragic that on such a beautiful day he should be so cold and still, all his love and gaiety and beauty gone for ever.

A slight breeze suddenly made the tear on her cheeks feel cold, as from the hawthorn hedge the wistful, descending lament of the willow warbler fell plaintively on the summer air.

Thee Luv

Ah wor nobbut a lass when Ah lost thi,
Ah'd just 'ed a babby an' 'aw,
Bud deep i'mi 'eart Ah con si thi,
Awtho' neaw it's so long ago.

Thad neet Ah knew summat 'ad 'appened,
An' long afoor t'bobby 'ad come,
Mi 'eart 'ad aw seized up inside mi,
Ah couldn'd feel nowt, Ah wor numb.

An' when thi said Tha wor deead luv
Why summat jus' snapped deep-inside,
Ah'd no farther use fer this cowd warld,
Ah jus' wished me an' t'babby 'ad died.

Bud later, when Ah'd done wi' greivin',
An' t'babby 'ad started te grow,
Ah med us a kind of existence…
Tho' it's ne'er bin same, tha mon know.

Ah've thried ta be 'appy an' cheerful
An' t'babby's a bonny lass neaw;
An' two-a-three chaps axed ta wed mi!
Bud nooan on um's like Thee someaw.

Some neets Ah lie thinkin' abeawt thi,
An' wish Tha wor 'ere bi mi side…
Bud Ah know it's na good wishin'
An' mi face in't' pilla I 'ide.

Ah wor nobbut a lass when Ah lost thi,
An' there's on'y mi pilla con know,
As deep in mi 'eart Ah still miss thi,
Awtho' neaw it's so long ago.

Eawr Christine's Weddin'

"It's na good tryin' to avoid it."
T'Missus sed wi' a baleful glare,
"Tha'll 'ev ta pud thi 'and i' thi pockit
Ur t'neighbours'll think as it's quer.

Afther aw, eawr Christine tha knows
Oo isn'd no ordnary lass,
Oo's bin t'college, an 'ed dancin' lessons,
An' oo's weddin i't'monied class.

Id marned be like Eva's weddin',
Aw rushed deawn at t'registherars,
Then afoor oo'd geet ring on 'er finger
Aw t'chaps 'ad rushed off eawt to t'bars.

Nay. eawr Christine's gooin' ta t'charch
In a luvly white Rolls Royce car;
It's na good sittin' theer, shakin' thi yead,
Refusin' worn'd ged thi sa far!

This time we're 'evin' a reyt do
Tha on'y getten Eva's o't'cheap
Because 'er an' thad foo' Willie Pickles
'Ad run afoor larnin' ta creep!

Oo's geddin' wed at St. Michael's,
An' evin t'red carpet an' aw!
An' bridesmaids, charch bells, an' fleawrs deawn booath aisles;
An' t'guest list is startin' ta grow."

"Neaw just a minute" Ah sed, "luv,
Ah know Christine's bin a good lass,
Bud bloody-ell-fire, what's this gooin' ta cost?
Tha knows luv, Ah'm nod med o' brass!"

"Thee watch thi tongue an' stop sweerin',
An' unless we're gooin' ta feight,
Thee watch thi tongue at reception an' aw,
An' when tha meks thi speech, speyk reyt!"

Well, Ah know when Ah've bin bested,
An' Ah know jus' when ta give in,
An' so fer t'best part o't'next seven months
Ah jus' watched mi wallit grow thin!

At last the big day drew near,
Ah wor sick of eytin' jam buts,
While t'Missus an' Christine dashed 'ere 'n' theer
Drivin' t'rest o't' family nuts.

Thur wor presents all o'er t'dresser,
An' frocks 'angin' off every dooar,
Cards an' notices wor on ev'ry ledge
An' boxes wor all o'er t'flooar.

O't'Frida' neet afoor t'weddin',
Ah wor just o' mi way ta t'club,
When t'Missus sed, "Oi! Wheer are ta gooin?
Come an' gi'me a 'and wi t'grub!"

Well Ah reckon thad wor t'last sthraw,
Ah sed, "Why should I 'elp wi't'grub?
Ah've tekken a bank looan eawt fer thad,
Thas 'ed id, Ah'm off deawn ta t'pub."

Mind,- when Ah geet back at midneet,
Oo wouldn'd even let me i'bed!
Sed oo wor betrayed in 'er eawr o' need,
Dam'd weddin' 'ad gone to 'er 'ead.

So, Ah med mi bed on t'sofa,
Bud Ah didn'd ged thad much sleep
'Cos t'Missus an' Christine geet up at four,
An' then Chrissy started ta weep!

"Neaw, wot's ta do luv I axed 'er?"
"Ah don't want ta leave 'ome!" Oo sed.
"Wod! After aw this money that's been spent!
Nay luv- thas just geet ta be wed!"

"Oh no! Oo 'asn'd, "sed t'Missus,
"It's never too late ta say no."
At thad Ah'd just ta be firm-like, an' sed,
"It's paid for, an' Christine'll go."

Well after thad t'were plain sailin',
T'sun shone an' t'bride fair looked a treat,
T'missus wor pleased we'd impressed the 'in-laws',
An' oo let mi i'bed thad neet!

Well, neaw that t'weddin' is over
An' we've photos of the big day,
Missus is 'appy, an' so's eawr Christine
Bud Ah'm nod...Ah've t'bank looan ta pay!

"A Mother's Lament"

Tha breyks mi 'eart when tha looks like thad wi' eyes so bonny an' blue,
An' Ah carned 'elp wonderin' little lass wod thee an' thi dad'll do;
Will ya forget 'eaw much Ah loved ya, when Ah'm lyin' cowd i't'greawnd
Fer two short months are aw Ah 'eve left since mi cruel disease wor feawnd.

Ah wor freetened when thi fost towd mi as Ah 'edn'd long to live,
Ah thowt of aw't things Ah could never do an' aw't love Ah couldn'd give.
Who'll brush thi long 'air an' watch thi grow, an' skryke when tha'r geddin' wed?
Who'll plaster thi knee when tha tumbles, an' who'll tuck thee up i'thi bed?

Tha'r ta young to tell as when tha'r three there'll on'y be thee an' Bill;
Ta young to tell that Ah carned pick thee up becus Ah'm feelin' thad ill.
Tha comes i' mi room to mi bedside, then tha slowly backs ta't dooar;
O! mi bonny, bonny little lass, Ah couldn't love thi no mooar!

Then Bill picks thee up an' brings thee back an' sits wi' thee on 'is knee;
An' when 'e settles mi deawn fer't neet 'e's gentle as 'e con be.
Bud while you're asleep Ah'm still wakken, an' missin' im i' mi bed,
An' wond'rin eaw long 'e'll stop lonely, or eaw long 'e'll wait to ged wed.

Ah've towd 'im 'e marned feel guilty, fer' 'e's on'y a young chap yet,
An' Ah've said as tha should 'ave a mam...then Ah wonder just who 'e'll get.
Wod if oo should be jealous o'thee? Fer thi say that looks jus' like me,
An' if they 'eve kids would thi love them best? O! why do Ah 'eve to dee?

When Gran browt mi' 'andbag this mornin', Ah looked at misel' i't'glass,
An Ah felt sa bitter later on, when Bill cawed me 'is bonny lass.
Fer neaw Ah know eaw 'e sis mi, cheeks grey an' eyes sunk deep wi' pain ,
Ay love! Ah'd give aw Ah 'ave i't' world if Ah could be bonny agen!

Bud nay, it's wicked ta think like thad, it's bein' selfish an' aw,
Ta lie 'ere thinkin' abeawt misel' when Ah should be thinkin' o' yo.
Fer Ah'm weel aware as nowt con bi done, Ah know Ah'm gooin' to dee,
Bud when thar grown up mi little lass, Ah just 'ope tha'll remember me.

The Gossip

Theer gus thad owd Mary Farquhar, oo's biggest gossip o't'row,
Oo's such a nooasy parker there's nowt thad oo doesn'd know.
Ah carned stand women thad gossip, Ah've mooar ta do wi' my day,
Such talk never passes my lips, Ah allus watch wod Ah say.
It's nod thad Ah'm stuck up or eawt, nod like Nellie next dooar
Oo looks sa posh when oo gus eawt while awt' street knows as they're poor.
An' Bill ,'er 'usband's, knockin' off a floozie from t'Rose an' Creawn,
It's na good thryin' to swank if thi other 'aif lets thi deawn.
O' couarse there's mooar than 'im o't'row, bud then, men carned be trusted,
They kid theirsel's us wives dorned know their shinin' armour's rusted.
Tek Jack as lives ad number six, 'e's in 'is seventh 'eaven
Fixin' t'back gate?...More like fixin' wi'er from number seven.
Nah theer's a woman needs watchin', aye, eve'ry time Ah'll bi bound
'Er bed-sheets are back i't'weshin' when t'coyl chap's bin on 'is reawnd.
An' their son Ronnie's just as bad, so it come as no surprise
To 'ear thad, "My confecioner lad" 'as med mooar than 'is bread rise.
Aye, 'e's cookin' 'is buns aw reyt, neaw 'e's payin' fer 'is fun
'E 'ed wi't'lass from number eight while engaged to 'er from one.
'Er dad created such a stink 'e made t'lass look a reyt foo'
'Cos id tarned eawt as id 'appened, oo wor i't'fam'ly way too!

Id must be nearly 'aif past ten 'cos t'post man's coming' up street,
Next door's geet nowt but bills agen, them's breawn envelopes aw reet.
They're cuttin' off their gas next week, Ah knows 'cos Ah geet letter,
Tho' id warned mine, Ah'ed a peek...well...t'postman should know better.
Them o't'other side dorned 'aif sheawt, they're t'noisiest lot o' t row,
Ah know wod their rows are abeawt, ev'ry ward comes clear thro'

'Ello, owd Mary's comin' back, oo looks reyt pleased wi 'ersel',
Ah'll bet 'er tongues bin gooin' clack, thad look - Ah con allus tell.
Ah'm glad Ah'm nod one ta gossip, Ah've mooar ta do wi my day,
Such talk never passes my lips, Ah allus watch wod Ah say.

T' Day We Teyched Mi 'Usband Ta Swim

Mi 'usband's reyt fit fer 'is age,
Bud fact thad 'e's fit doesn'd mather,
Wod meks me allus goo into a rage
Ist' fact thad 'e carned stand cowd watter.

Whenever we've bin to t' seaside
Cecil's stopped 'igh an' dry onta t'beach,
It's na matter if it's 'igh or low tide,
'E'll do owt ta keep eawt of id reach.

E'll goo a' fetch tay or ice creams
An' 'e'll mind piles o' clooathes aw day,
In fact 'e's prepared ta do owt it seems
Just ta keep eawt o' cowd watter's way.

Bud last year we persuaded 'im,
When we aw went ta th' oliday camp,
Thad 'e warned ta owd ta be teyched ta swim
Even tho' id ud mean geddin' damp.

So we took 'im deawn to t'pool-side
Wur 'e slowly dipped one finger in,
When 'e feawnd id wor warm 'is smile grew wide
An' 'e promised ad last 'e'd goo in.

So Rebecca took 'er grandad
Fer some trunks, an' 'e chose some bright green.
"Well," Ah said "Cecil, Ah'll sey this owd lad,
If tha carned swim ad least tha'll be seen."

We took 'im in at shalla' end,
Wor 'e bravely walked deawn toddlers' slope:
We thowt all us problems wor at an end,
Bud wi eawr pupil thad wor some 'ope.

Cos when 'e ducked 'is 'ead under
'Is fawse teeth floated eawt inta t'pool,
Bud thad wor nowt to 'is second blunder
Becos thad med 'im look a reyt fool .

Tha sis, 'e'd started jumpin' in,
An' pullin' 'issel' eawt onta t'side,
Bud trouble wor Cecil's waist; id wor thin
An' t'green trunks just a little bit wide.

'E 'adn't tightened t'little cord
An' t'trunks dropped as 'e pulled 'issel eawt:
If folks lookin' on 'ad bin feelin' bored
Neaw thi started ta whistle an' sheawt.

Aw pale an' pink, 'is bum popped eawt:
So Ah went wi' eawt 'esitation
An' I 'auled up t'back, then 'is front fell eawt
An embarassin' situation.

Id wor then thad t'others left us,
T'green trunks 'ad tarned their faces red,
They decided from then on they'd watch us,
Afoor other disclosures wor med.

They wor, agen bi my Cecil,
Cos bi then 'e wor thryin' ta swim,
Bud as 'e's blind i' one eye, poor owd lad,
'E couldn'd si t'young lass swimmin' to'ard 'im.

They crashed 'ead to 'ead i't'watter,
An' 'e thowt 'e wor gooin' ta dreawn
Wur 'e grabbed an' 'e clawed didn'd mather,
Just as long as 'e didn'd go deawn.

'E didn'd…instead 'e come up,
Lookin' toothless an' aw drippin' wet
An' 'e 'eld in 'is 'and a bikini cup,
Id wor Cecil's best exposure yet.

Ah plunged in then ta rescue 'im,
While t'lass stood by, arms coverin' 'er loss.
"Come on eawt Cec" Ah sed, mi meawth aw prim.
So 'e did, cos 'e knows just who's boss.

Neaw Cec's swimmin' days are o'er,
An' once mooar 'e just watches fro' t'beach.
'Is green trunks are lyin' tucked in a drawer
An' temptation stays well eawt o' reach.

Reunion

"Mother why don't you come down and stay with me until you are really capable of looking after yourself properly again?" Joan asked. Silence. Then Agnes began her usual evasive reply…"Perhaps next year dear…" "Mother, you have just been in hospital, you need a rest now. Please come, I promise it won't be like last time. Don't forget I'm a lady of leisure now."

The last time was six years ago, when Joan was still working; and Agnes, who hated cities, had spent a hot summer month cooped up in two airless rooms not daring to go out, missing her own lovely home and garden. She had enjoyed the evenings, but had been making excuses ever since, delaying a repetition of the experience.

Joan was still speaking at the other end of the line, "…so I will sort out a train and pick you up from Euston on Tuesday. Sorry I can't bring you down but John isn't used to the new flat yet. Oh! and by the way mother do be tactful about his age won't you? Poor darling, he feels bad enough about being blind and gets so jealous; he's afraid I will run off with the first sighted man under seventy-five that I meet."

"Joan don't you think you have enough on your hands…"she began. "Mother, he isn't an invalid. He's witty and clever and gallant and very upper crust. This time I know you will approve. We've only been together six months, but I feel I've known him all my life. Look, I shall have to go he's downstairs in the hall. He's got the door-bell sorted out but not the lifts. See you Tuesday, but I'll phone again first. Bye…"

Agnes put the receiver down with a sigh. Joan had always been impulsive. She had run off to London all those years ago with a long-haired drummer, now she was living with a man twenty-seven years her senior, "Living with", the expression was quite shameful, still she had carved out a good career for herself, and after all she was forty-eight so there was no risk of children. She made up her mind, she would go. This John sounded quite respectable.

She missed a man's company. It was seven years now since Robert had died. Dear Robert, so kind and comforting, right from the start he had cosseted her: then when he had asked her to marry him and she had sobbed in his arms and confessed that she was already pregnant he had asked no questions but had repeated his offer. She still wept tears of self-pity at her loss.

The journey to London had been less exhausting than she imagined. Joan had met her at Euston and they had driven to The Barbican where they had tea on the terrace, Agnes thought it was quite gay and continental.

Arriving at the flat she nodded her approval, it was beautiful, this time it was going to be different. Joan settled her mother in an armchair, gave her coffee and a pile of magazines, kissed Agnes briefly and rushed off to pick up John from his club, calling over her shoulder as she went, "Sorry, but I'm late. Won't be long, it's only a mile away. Make yourself comfortable."

As the door closed Agnes smiled, it was nice to be taken care of again. She slipped off her shoes and leaned back, she took a sip of coffee, but grimacing she put down the cup, it was far too strong. She thumbed idly through one of the glossy magazines, it was filled with outlandish clothes at exorbitant prices, she replaced it on the table and wandered barefoot across to the window.

The flat overlooked a small park, beyond which the traffic appeared to be moving silently; a police car threading its way through at great speed, its blue light flashing lost all urgency, divorced from its klaxon.; it looked quite pretty.

What a pity John could not see such an interesting panorama, this really was a lovely part of the city. Turning from the window she became curious, what did he look like; Robert was sixty-three when he died and was beginning to look quite old; but seventy-five, she shuddered. She looked round for photographs and saw some on a beautiful walnut side-table whose centrepiece was a large blue and white porcelain bowl filled with fresh pink and yellow roses. She picked up one of the photographs in a silver frame, it showed a well-dressed military looking man, with a small moustache, holding the harness of a guide dog, of course that was probably how Joan had met him, she had been organising campaigns for years. As she replaced the frame Agnes stooped to smell the roses and it was as she lifted her, head that she saw it.

Dear God it couldn't be. Propped against a small ginger-jar was an unframed, sepia snapshot of three young pilots, posing beside a Spitfire; as she gazed numb with horror, two of the faces blurred, but the third, that of a tall young man with a fair moustache smiled mockingly at her. She clutched the brass edging of the table, it was him, it was the same man, only younger. After years of respectability, and now he had surfaced again, living with his own daughter, she felt sick, drained; this was the kind of thing that only happened in

Greek tragedies or silly novels. It couldn't be true. But it was true. With a rush of memory, that she had thought was buried forever, she could feel again the brush of the soft moustache, the roughness of his uniform against her thighs; she remembered the haste. She had felt cheap and used, and she hadn't even known his name. What could she do.

She must leave, that was certain. But she couldn't go without telling Joan. Nor could she ruin her daughter's life. She would stay. She would say nothing. She would bear the burden alone; after all it was her wrong doing...hers and his. Supposing he recognised her voice...what rubbish...she became conscious of a bell ringing. She picked up the phone, but the ringing continued.

The door slowly opened. Two policemen stood outside. One of them came in. "Mrs. Derbyshire," he said. She nodded and her heart raced furiously. The policeman came towards her and held her arm, comfortingly. "There has been an accident." \

"Is he dead?" she asked, trying to keep the hope she felt in her heart away from her eyes.

"No" came the answer. "But they are keeping him in hospital overnight, he is in shock, but asked if we would break the news. He would be grateful under the circumstances Mrs. Derbyshire if you could wait until tomorrow to meet him. You see he was standing on the pavement waiting for her when he heard the crash, then he heard the crowd talking and somebody from his club took him along to the hospital."

"You mean...it's Joan. How is she, is she badly hurt."

He led her to a chair. God how he hated this bit. No matter how many times he had to say it he still felt like running away. "I'm sorry Mrs. Derbyshire, your daughter died instantly."

The Eccentric

Rumpled clothes, shoes down at heel, she appears not to feel
The icy winter's bitter cold on legs that are too fat and old
To be without a covering...shabby thing.

Uncombed-hair, coat open wide, she appears, steps outside,
Crosses the street without a glance, causing the passing cars to dance
On the road's icy surfacing...silly thing.

Fingers fumble with the cold, she appears poor and old,
Pleading with the butcher fat, for bits of this and bits of that.
Grateful for almost anything...pathetic thing.

Back once more at her front door she appears not so poor,
Smiles with gentle satisfaction, business-like and geared for action
Delighted now with everything...crazy thing.

With tails aloft, mouths open wide, cats appear from every side,
She coos, caresses, pets and feeds and ministers to all their needs,
To their lives hers dedicating...kindly thing.

When spring arrives with melted snow, she appears not to know;
Bottles stand outside her door, inside her cats stretched on the floor.
Stretched around her body mouldering...poor thing.

A Broody Ballad

It's 'appened ageean. Ten times Ah've bin catched.
Mi mam's allus said wi wor booath weel matched.
By gum, when Ah met 'im Ah'd no idea then,
When 'e sed 'e liked kids we'd end up wi' ten.

Ten. Ah ask ya! Ah feel jus' like a rabbit.
Some fooaks plan kids. Wi' us it's an 'abit!
Mi sisther mooans cos oo carned 'ev ony,
An' 'ere Ah'm frettin' becos Ah've ta monny.

Wi started us fost just afoor wi wor wed,
"It's a reyt fruitful start," Mi owd Grandma sed.
Ah little knew then jus' wot th' 'arvest ud be
Fost time Ah giv' in o'mi mam's best settee.

Eawr Edie as moans 'as bin thryin' fer years
While Ah've thried ta get shut wi' jumpin' deawn stears.
Ah didn'd tell my Bert, 'e'd a thowt Ah'd gone leet,
Cos Ah didn'd get shut, Ah just 'urt boath feet

Once somebody sed as 'ot baths 'us do trick,
Then Ah thried castor oil, That jus' med mi sick.
So neaw Ah've gi'n in, an' Ah leave id to fate,
It's neaw getten to t'stage when wi dornd need to mate!

Aw Ah need ta do neaw is jus' wesh 'is socks.
Aye, my chasity belt is needin' new locks.
Mi mam, oo despairs, ses 'e's jus' like a bull.
'Is archer pal Fred ses 'is quiver's ta full.

Bud mi owd Grandma ses as there's no disgrace
While 'e's tippin' 'is coil in 'is own coil place.
Aw t'same, tha carned blame mi fer 'evin a dream
As we'll stop afoor we've us own football team.

Ada Duckett An' Dr. Flynn

Eawr docthur wor a gradely mon, 'is name wor Michael Flynn,
An' a nicer natured fellah Ah'll bet tha's never sin.
'E wor a mine o'comfort, 'e ladled id bi' t'bucket,
Until 'e geet a patient whose name wor Ada Duckett,

When Ada gazed into 'is een oo nea'ly threw a fit.
'Er mind went like a fruit machine; three lemons 'e wor it,
T'mon uv 'er dreams, 'ere ad last, oo couldn'd wait ta be ill,
Oo stood eawtside i't'pourin' rain ta give 'ersel' a chill.

Oo went to t'surg'ry twice a week, sometimes mebbe mooar;
T'poor mon could 'ear 'er in 'is sleep, knockin' on 'is dooar.
"Ah've geet a lump. A've getten a cowd. Ah find id 'ard ta sleep.
When Ah weear mi wooly ganzy, mi skin begins ta creep."

"Con Ah 'ev some coolin' peawthers, some lotion er some pills?"
'E couldn'd prescribe 'em fast enough ta keep up wi' 'er ills.
One week oo couldn'd stop sweatin', while next oo 'ed 'ot flushes
An wod oo thried ta show 'im fair browt 'im eawt i' blushes.

'E geet sick o't'lame excuses thad Ada conjured up.
Like when oo geet a wobbly 'and an' couldn'd owd 'er cup,
Or keyked o'er on 'er ankle, or banged 'er funny booan.
"Please Mrs. Duckett," Michael said, "Please leave me alooan."

"There's nowt ad' aw that's wrong wi' thi, so just stop aw this lyin'."
But still oo kept on 'asselin, still oo kept on thryin'.
Said 'er lugs warched: oo'd 'eayd warch an' gripin' in 'er belly;
Oo spent 'er neets wi' med'cine books, give o'er watchin' telly.

Poor chap felt moithered, couldn'd sleep, 'is 'ealth 'ad gone ta t'dogs,
'E getten thad warked up one neet 'e up an' popped 'is clogs.
Oo couldn'd fancy t'new chap an' so oo 'ed ta chuck it;
An' as 'er life seemed woth nowt neaw, Ada Duckett took it.

Neaw bi some fluke o' fortune, oo wor buried i't next plot
Ta' t'docther sleepin' peaceful, like a babby in id cot.
Till Ada, still i' limbo, still conscious of 'is chaerms,
Passed thro' t'muck 'er last request, "Con ta gi me owt fer t'waerms?"

Owd Nick

or 'The Triumph Of Sin'

Mi Uncle Nick's bin a bad un,
'E wor weel named sooah thi sed,
A devil fro' t'minute as 'e wor born
In mi Grandma's owd, big, brass bed.

Poor lass laid pushin' an' shovin'
Fer t'best part o't'day an' aw neet,
An' then instead of emergin' eyd fost,
'E punsed 'is way eawt wi' both feet.

Mi Gran'ma 'ad eight or nine kids.
Ah'm not sure, 'cos some on um deed,
But thi couldn'd get shut o' Nicholas,
'E wor allus theer to feed.

'E went to t'schoo' when 'e wor five,
But 'e mut weel o' gone at six,
'Cos 'e used to 'ide i't'closet aw day,
'E wor allus up to some tricks.

An' when thi geet 'im i't'classroom
Instead of 'im doin' 'is sums,
'E'd mek ink pellets wi' blottin' papper,
An' flick 'em at t'other kid's bums.

'E'd umpteen jobs when 'e left schoo',
But nooan on um took 'is fancy,
'E spent aw day swillin' beer i't' pub.
Folks thowt 'is prospects wor chancy.

But then 'e 'ad a stroke o' luck,
As fellas like 'im offen do,
'E put a lass inta t'fam'ly way;
But mi Uncle Nick wor no foo'.

'Er parents booath objected,
But 'is ardour thi couldn't kill.
He insisted "o' doin' right by 'er"
...Afther aw 'er father owned t'mill.

Well, then 'e didn'd 'ave to wark,
That suited young Nick deawn to greawnd.
'E no longer spent 'is days swillin' ale
As whisky wor better 'e feawnd.

'E then tarned 'is eye to women.
So to tek up some of 'is day
Uncle Nick wor med one o't'directors
...An' 'e supped aw't'money away.

By time mi Aunt Mary left 'im,
To go to 'er 'eavenly 'ome,
Mi owd Uncle Nick wor deawn on 'is luck.
'E'd on'y t'streets left to roam.

One-bi-one 'is family deed,
An' 'e'd become lonely an' poor.
Mi mam said, "Ah'm nod 'avin' 'im in 'ere
'E's not settin' foot through my door!

'E's 'ad 'is chances 'as Uncle Nick,
An' 'e's not tekkin' us for fools!"
Weeks later oo could 'ave etten 'er words,
'E won thousands on't' football pools!

Well, then there were no 'owdin'im.
'E took a young bride to 'is bed.
Mi mam, fair disgusted, said to 'im,
"In eight or nine months tha'll be dead."

Though oo allus said as virtue
Is its own reward i' this life,
Ah'm neaw beginin' ta wonder,
If it wor to stop me enjoyin' life.

Because neaw oo's lyin' buried
An' Ah carned believe wod oo said,
For Nick is sittin' 'ere eytin' my grapes,
An' watchin' while Ah dee i'bed.

Never Na Mooar

Never na mooar Ah'll si thi face, never na mooar.
Nor nestle-up i' thi fond embrace, nod ony mooar.
When neet faws Ah'm lonely an' mi bed's ower wide.
An' t'darkness seems endless wi'eawt thee bi mi side.
Neaw there's one place ad table wheer once there wor two,
An' as th'eawsework is less there's nowt much left ta do.
Life's empty beawt thee love an' Ah still connad see
Why tha went off wi Barbara afther six year wi' me

Never na mooar Ah'll miss thi face, never na mooar.
Nor want thi sittin' bi t'fireplace, nod ony mooar.
When neet faws Ah'm off gaddin' ta t' pub wi' mi pals
An' dark neets are romantic fer us good-time gals.
Neaw Ah never lay table, Ah'm tekken eawt ta dine;
An' Ah couldn'd care less if mi windas dorned shine.
Neaw mi life's changed fer t'better Ah just connad see
Why Ah whinged when wi parted an' tha set mi free.

Who Wants Your Christmas Pudding?

When our five children were growing up we lived in a lovely thirteen-roomed Victorian house and managed to fill it reasonably well. However, on Christmas morning each year, you could, if you had visited, be forgiven for thinking that you were in a rooming house in downtown Calcutta. Because then, our family of seven was joined by Aunt Edith, my sister Dinah, Ian her husband and daughter Jacqueline, and Aunty May. These six came for Christmas lunch, whilst other relatives and visitors also dropped in during the day.

I loved cooking, and annually prepared a six-course meal. But each year I was haunted by the fear that my white sauce for the Christmas pudding would lump at the last minute.

It never did, but each year I expected that it would... and so one year I took the coward's way out and bought a packet from the supermarket.

The great day arrived and when the pudding was due, I carried it from the kitchen, gloriously aflame to well-fed cheers. I then brought in the sauce and having served everyone told them to tuck in whilst I went back to the kitchen to put the coffee on.

When I returned to the table I found everyone sitting silently with untouched sweets before them.

"You shouldn't have waited for me" I began...but Peter, my eldest son, interrupted.

"Mum" he said, "It tastes awful."

"It can't" I said, "Joe Colman made it."

Ian, who also liked cooking, jumped to my rescue. "Have you got the packet?" he asked.

When I retrieved it from the waste bin the mystery was solved.

Unused to buying ready-made sauce, I had inadvertantly bought a fish sauce.

To loud laughter, I collected the offending portions, rinsed them under the tap, and redistributed them with hastily-prepared custard.

Edith, who was deaf, added to the hilarity by telling me that Jacqueline had laughed until her massacre had run down her cheeks.

The whole episode went down in the Snape annals as the day that mother washed the Christmas pudding.

Thoughts of a Pantheist*

It's strange to think that when I die
No more I'll see a summer sky,
Nor feel the cooling summer's breeze
And gaze with wonder at the trees.
It's strange to think that nevermore
I'll hear the sea caress the shore
And watch the seagulls on the wing,
Or listen to the skylark sing.

Would that my soul and ear and eye
Could ever with the songbirds fly,
There to exist for evermore,
Whilst others knock at heaven's door;
I doubt they'll find there's nothing there
That with earth's beauty can compare.
My creed is not in psalters found
But in the blessings all around;

My praise is not to church confined
Nor lying unsung in my mind;
But grows with every passing year,
Enriching life, deriding fear.
I give my praise to God and love
The land beneath. the sky above,
And ever cherish my brief span
On this fair earth He gave to man.

* One who identifies God with the natural world

Summer Meadow

O! How we loved
To walk through fragrant meadows, you and I,
And listen to the skylark as he sang
So far above us in the summer sky.

We were in love,
And as we strolled the dusty paths were sweet
With honeyed-clover, and the meadow scents
Beguiled our senses and our sandalled feet.

Then, as we strayed,
And lay together hidden in the grass
To watch white clouds drift across perfect blue,
Like any other lovers, lad and lass, O! How we loved.

Twinch

One o' mi grandchilder's just geet back off an 'oliday 'i Florida. Oo come runnin' inta th'eawse deein' to tell me aw abeawt id, an while oo were talkin' Ah thowt eaw wi used to think ussel' lucky if wi getten to Blackpoo' fer a day. But Ah carred quiet, 'cos fooalk get sick of 'earin' ya 'arpin' on abeawt eaw things used to be.

When oo'd gone Ah med mi tay an' switched t'telly on, fer company, but Ah warn'd lis'nin', Ah were thinkin' abeawt Twinch, an' eaw at 'er age Ah used to think as thad were t'mooast excitin' place i't'warld. Thad were my Disneyland.

Id were but a ten-minute walk fro'eawr 'eawse; tha went through t'guinnel, deawn White Ash Lane, tarned reyt, an' tha were theer.

T'fost thing tha si were Smithy Bruck, t'gateway to 'eaven. Id were on'y abeawt two'o' three yard wide an' na mooar nor a foot deep i't'breawnest bits. O'course this were afoor id were aw foul'd up wi't'chemical warks up Brookside usin' id to tek id dregs an' stink away. Tha'd ne'er credit id but t'chap as owned id were med a "Sir"…still, that's life. Ony rooad id wor a cleyn bruck then, wi' fleaw'rs growin' deawn id banks, an' tiddlers an' sticklebacks 'idin' i't'shaddas.

T'bruck sidled past five white-weshed cottages, aw wi' little gardens full o' fleaw'rs, tha could eyther cross id o'er a narra wood footbridge wi' oyls in id planks, or wade cobblestooaned ford, weer t'carts gooin' to th'owd papper mill at t'other end o' Twinch used to cross. I' summer tha could sometimes walk across t'ford wi' thi shoon on, but if there'd bin a lot o' rain, t'bruck swelled an' were a ragin' torrent thad once or twice weshed t'bridge away an' flooded t'cottages. After t'ford, t'watter dropped like a babby Niagara ten feet deawn to a deep pool afoor t'bruck widened eawt ageean. I' summer tha could sit o't'warm stooans an' dangle thi feet i't'pool, but i' winter when id were jet black wi' yella frothy edges, tha'd give id a wide berth if tha'd onny sense.

On t'reyt 'and side o't'bruck were an owd grassed o'er tip, an' sometimes we'd find a dreawned, maggoty rat in t'watter, an' we'd aw stand reawnd lovin' id evil look, an' 'atin' id 'orrable yella teeth. If there were a lot of us we'd climb up t' tip an' slide deawn t'dusty bit i't'middle, then we'd get pasted when we getten 'ooam, for bein' mucky an' weearin' t'backsides eawt of us briches.

Just past t'tip on a flat bit o' greawnd there were three mooar cottages standin a bit back fro't' bruck, an' th'owd woman as lived i't'middle un 'ed fruit trees in 'er garden, an' oo'd bang wi'er posser o't'th'owd tin bath thad 'ung on 'er back wa', if oo see us pinchin' 'er apples.

But we liked t'fost 'eawse best weer an owd sailor lived. Ah'm sorry neaw as we never axed 'im abeawt 'is travels, but 'e didn'd interest us; it were 'is big green parrot as 'e kept in a cage under t'lilac tree as we wanted to talk to. If we'd gone 'ooam an said some o'them wards as that parrot knew, we'd o' getten cleawted reawnd th'ear 'oyl.

Deawn thad end o' Twinch tha'ad paradise o' booath sides o't' lane becos' th'owd papper mill were o't'left.

Apart for t'big stooan gate posts, a bit o't'gate 'eawse, an' t'cracked stooan bed wi't'rusty remains o't'big engine, there were nowt much o't'mill left to look at; but for playin' in yon, Disneyland couldn'd owd a candle. Eawr imaginations run riot in id ruined ups an' deawns of owd bricks an' stooans, grown o'er wi' ferns an' rosebay willa'erbs, elderberry bushes an' pussy willas. At t'top side were a big lodge wi' two swans, bullrushes, pink an' white watter lilies an' fish. Nod tiddlers, real fish, big uns, an' if tha were quiet an' knew weer to look, tha could lie o't'bank an' tickle 'em.

T'lodge 'ad two overflows; one were a biggish watterfall as went under t'lane an' joined t'bruck; t'other med a long narra pool that stretched back ta t'bridge, but on a higher level non t'lane. Sometimes i' summer id nearly dried up, but nod offen 'cos id were shaded wi' big trees. Ah liked this bit best, an' in t'summer 'olidays we'd set off in t'mornin' wi' some butties in a breawn papper bag, a pop bottle full o'watter, a jam jar wi' string reawnd top for carryin'id, an' if we were lucky, a penny fishin' net fro' t'top shop. We'd stop theer 'til taytime; fishin' for tiddlers, catchin' frogs, dammin' up bits o't'pool to put owt in as we'd catched, skimmin' stooans, paddlin' or just lyin' back i't'sun.

Eh...Things aren'd wod they used to be, but then, neyther is Twinch. Ah've bin back twice, but Ah's go no mooar.

T'fost time Ah took my childer deawn. Ah'd offen towd 'em abeawt id but we were aw disappointed. T'cottages 'ad aw bin pulled deawn, trees chopped, t'bruck stunk an' were littered wi' bits of owd prams an' such like. T'lodge 'ad bin drained so my pond an't'watterfall ad booath gone, an't'mill were shut off wi' barbed wire.

Then t'other week i't'local papper Ah read as aw t'Civic Society 'ad cleyned id up. Ah were off like a shot.

Neaw there's nowt theer but a rooad an' a fenced off bruck, wi' banks as bare as a clinic.

T'motorway's mooar interestin'.

Thi do say as tha should never go back, Ah suppooas it sarves me reyt. Onyrooad Ah'm gooin' to t'travel agents tamorn to get me some o'them brochures abeawt Florida.

Ah might go next year...if Ah'm still 'ere.

A Lancashire Pub

There's Lancashire pubs, an' there's Lancashire pubs,
Just like there's fooak an' fooak;
An' there's mony a lot o' warkin' mons' clubs
Whur t'wives like to sit an' tooak.

Bud if thar a mon who warks damned 'ard aw day
An' carned wait for thad fost swalla,
If tha caws into t'pub afoor thi tay
Well, t'pint-oyl licks posh rooms 'olla.

If thi 'ands are mucky nob'dy keears,
Tha con wipe thi gob o' thi sleeve,
An' tha'r nod ta freetened to sit o't'cheears
Fer t'sake o't'muck as tha'll leave.

I't'pint-oyl, tha sis, women just dorned come in,
Tha worned need to watch wod tha sez,
An' nob'dy minds if th'ale runs deawn thi chin,
An' nob'dy keears wod tha 'es.

Fer 'ere in a Lancashire pub thar thissen
There's no need ta pud on feawse airs,
Tha con spit an' sweer an argue wi' men
Abeawt proper monly affairs.

Bud tha knows we're gooin' ta 'ev ta keep watch,
Fer pint-oyls are growin' ta few,
An' mooast pubs 'ev awready gone thad top-notch
Thad a dropped aitch tarns t'barmaid blue.

Fer if tha goes in wi thi wife after tay,
Tha's allus ta weear a cleyn shart,
Tha'es to speyk reyt, or believe me tha'll pay,
Why, oo worned even let thi fart.

Aye, some modern pubs mek thi feel ill-at-ease
Because they've geet thad tarted-up,
Still, Lancashire pubs'll allus please
While they've Lancashire beer to sup.

Music i'Lancashire
(A Weyver's Symphony)

Music, i'Lancashire, why mon, t'wor aw reawnd,
It 'overed i' th'air an' it drummed onta t'greawnd

Fost movement, allegro, aye, we wor reyt fast
In obeyin' t'demands o'th'ooter's leawd blast;
An' walkin' ta wark a crescendo o' seawnd
Grew, fro' th'undreds o' clogs aw clatterin' o't'greawnd.
Tutti, aw together i't'big weyvin' shed
We warked, while looms played eawt a fugue in us 'ead.
Staccato, wor t'noise med bi th'owd pickin' stick,
Con motto, wi' movement, t'shuttle flew quick;
An' be'ind aw t'chatterin' looms throbbed a seawnd
Sostenuto, t'wor th'engine, wot tarned t'shaftin' reawnd
Pulsatin' i't'backgreawnd, smooth seawnd aw day long,
Legato is t'word that describes it i' song.

Then as t'vanishin' sun proclaimed time fer tay
T'wer Morendo as th'engine slowed deawn fer t'day.

Gooin' eawt through t'gates, t'second movement begun,
Andante we moved, we wor too tired to run.
Maestoso, majestic, though weary we war,
As we med fer us 'ooams near an' far;
Then a nice wesh i't'sink when wi'd 'ed us tay,
Fer a nod in t'cheear would mean th'end o't'day.

Next, scherzo, third movement of us day come then,
Vivace wi felt, booath women an' men.
Arpeggios o'pigeons would fly up to t'sky,
An lads o' street corners watch lasses go by
Wi' grace, grazioso, aloof or aw shy.
Young men gazed fuocco, wi' fire in their eye;
While o'er t'cobbles an' t'chimneys floated eawt t'seawnd
O' cantabile organs an' choirs 'eaven beawnd.
Then when t'dusk wor fawin' we aw said goodneet,
An' drunks rowlled larghetto up t'middle o't' street.

T'finale, t'last movement o't' warkin' mon's day.
Depended o't' key used fer wark an' fer play;
Fer when t'stars wer twinklin' i't' th'eavens above,
Men, impassionato, would pray or mek luv.
Tunes played eawt i' life are oft' 'ard to assess,
Bud each mon lives a symphony eawt, no less.

The Storm

The sparkling waters of the bay
In lambent sun-kissed beauty lay
Held safe by cliffs, warm, chalk-white arms,
Whose golden gorse and wind-swept farms
Dozed 'neath a sky of azure blue;
Where gulls with wide-spread, white wings flew,
Seeking, soaring, jubilant, free,
Skimming the surface of the sea.
Blue wavelets gently nudged the shore,
Coyly wthdrew then nudged once more;
Artfully gaining from the land,
Sucking in shingle, shells and sand.

Filling the bay the greedy sea
Began to murmur restlessly.
The gorse high on the cliffs grew pale,
A wind sprang up became a gale.
The sky was dark, the white birds gone,
The waves now angry beating on
The steadfast cliffs with all their might,
The day had died, o'erwhelmed by night.

The sea still thundered, raged and tore
At cliffs and rocks and ravaged shore.
Rain from the sky, spume from the sea
All beat as one cacophony.
The steel-grey waves with murderous roar
Crashed and retreated, came once more,
All nature's force on pillage bent.
When day returned the storm was spent.
The cliffs shone clean and fresh and white,
The waves retreated with the night.
But scattered wide across the bay
Sad relics of the storm still lay
And by the rock-pools newly-filled
Limp, broken birds the storm had killed
Lay prey to maggot, rot and sun;
As like the storm their course was run.

Night in the City

The sleepless city dozes fitfully;
Its transient population like the tide
Which on some rocky shore engulfs it, or
Recedes to leave behind its detrius.
The ghostly homeless; jostling for doorways,
Seeking warmth in rags and bags and boxes;
Or alleys, where profligate restauranteurs
Consign to stinking bins their scraps of food.
Under bridges and flyovers, like some
Dickensian flotsam, cold, gaunt and hungry;
Huddled in destitution, misery,
Or the dark neterworld of drunkeness.
Once they were moved, but now too few police
Mix artfully with the verminous throngs,
Or infiltrate exclusive, basement clubs
To track purveyors of cocaine and crack.
Outside deserted streets are split apart
By siren wails, as ambulances race
To rescue wretched, erstwhile revellers,
Now maimed or dying, who have paid the price
To pushers, drink or drugs or alley thugs;
Whilst boldly on the kerb, the girls of vice
Following their ill-chosen calling, tout;
And pimps in flashy cars keep wary watch.

Up West, smart theatres and concert halls
Have long since jettisoned their cultured crowds
To taxis, cars and comfortable homes.
All that now remain are office-cleaners,
Street-sweepers and the late-night burger stands,
Steaming oases in luminous mist.
And rolling through the night, ubiquitous,
The mighty press spews news, views and gossip,
Parcels and bales it, sending vans in fleets,
With cargoes through the silent city streets
To corner booths, where inky sheets await
The ritual buyers of the new day's rush.

A Trip ta t'Brewery

T'club allus 'es two-o-three local eawtins a year as weel as t'big do i'summer. So tha con imagine thad when Arthur 'Esketh's lad Bill organized a trip ta t'brewery wheer 'e warks, t'lads were feytin' fer places

We went i'January, to cheer us aw up afther us Christmas an' New Year 'ang overs, an' by gow id wor a cowd neet too. Brewer Bailey as wor waitin' eawtside to tell us when t'chara' tarned up, kept nippin'in fer a drop o'th' 'ard stuff to keep 'issel' warm; an as damn' thing wor 'aif an 'our late 'e wor weel oiled afoor we'd even set off.

Ned Foster who teks us on aw t'local does is allus late. Every year we say we'll ged somebody else, bud tha knows wod it's like, we aw feel sorry for 'im. Poor owd Ned an' 'is bus are booath fawin' ta bits an' we carned find id in us 'earts to seck 'em.

Onyrooad, when at last it tarned up we set off wi' booath Ned an' 'is bus wheezin an' splutterin' aw t'way up broo, bud as t'brewery's nobbut three mile off we didn'd think as id would tek us long, even at t'speed as Ned's bus chugs at. So 'aif an 'our later when somebody said it felt like we wor gooin' o'er a ploughed field, Ah looked through t'winda' an' by the 'eck we wor an' aw. Owd Ned 'ad missed a tarnin' an' decided to tek a short cut. Id wor a good job id 'ad bin freezin' 'ard aw day, else we might o' bin stuck i't'middle o'that field aw neet.

When we did ged theer they took us aw reawnd, an' to a set o' boozers like us id wor reyt intherestin'. When we went inta t'big fermentin' rooms wi stainless steel vats, big enough ta wesh 'aif a dozen elephants in aw at same time, we wor aw stuck fer wards at seet o'thad much beer i'one shop. Then Joe Mannin, t'club's prize knocker-back brokken t'silence.

"By gum lads!" 'e said in an awe-sthruck voice, "Ah'll tell thi wod, dreawnin' ud be a pleasure i'theer."

But t'bit as Ah's allus remember wor when they took us i't'place wheer th' 'ops an' thad are aw kept. Id wor a big room, wi secks piled aw reawnd twa's, an' thad cleyn even t'missus couldn'd o'feawnd owt to pick up. Then t'chap as wor tekkin' us reawnd said in 'is reyt posh voice,

"Now I will turn the lights off for a few minutes." We aw stood theer i't'dark wontherin' wod wor gooin' on, bud when 'e put leets back on we soon feawnd eawt. Wa's wor covered 'aif way up wi cockroaches. T'place wor wick we'em; theawsands on'em! Aw battlin' fer places, like t'lads on a Set'day afthernoon ad a big match. Brewer Bailey thowt as 'e wor 'ev'in' one of 'is do's an' we'd ta calm 'im deawn an' tell 'im as we could aw see 'em too. T'chap said thad woddever they did they couldn'd get shut, so t'leets wor allus kept on aw time i'thad room.

Well, when we'd sin ev'rythin' there wor ta see, they took us to a little room thad looked a bit like t'local caff; wi' little tables wi checked-papper table cloths and reyt uncomfortable lookin' cheears.

Then t'chap said 'e 'oped we'd feawnd id interestin', an' 'oped we'd enjoy t'rest o't'neet, then 'e towd us to sit us'sel's deawn an 'e disappeared.

"Well" Fred Brierly said, lookin' reyt pleased. "Id looks like we're gooin' ta ged a cup o' tay lads."

Thad would probably o' suited 'im awreyt becus 'e sups thad little 'e mut weel be T.T. But t'rest on us could 'ave 'it 'im.

"Nay Bill!" another mon said, "Surely they'll give us a free sup worned they? They'd never miss id eawt o' yon great bath tub back theer."

"Thee wait thi eh-uppin,'" Bill said.

Well, wod come next knocked us aw fer six.

They fotched some thrays o'beer in an' when we'd aw 'ed a pint Bill said, "Well…come on lads…this is wod you've aw bin waitin' for isn'd id? Come on! sup up! Ya con 'eve as much as ya fancy."

It wor like a birthday an' Christmas aw rowlled inta one.

Fred Brierley wor th'on'y one suppin' lemonade.

But thad neet wor t'fost time Ah've ever sin Ian Skinner three sheets ta t'wind; 'e usually meks a gill last aw neet, an allus goes i't'gents when they're collectin' or sellin' raffle tickets. It's nod thad 'e's'ard up, it's just thad, like Les Murphy ses, "'E's thad tight is arse squeaks."

They on'y give us three quarters of an 'our, bud we did justice ta t'club's good name, an' like Frank Randle used ta say, "We supped some ale thad neet."

Heaw't be, when they cawed time there were mooar nor one or two 'ed ta be 'elped onta t'bus.

Ah fer one carned remember much abeawt geddin' 'ooam, bud Ah con recollect somebody askin' Ned if 'e'd stop on t'top rooad wheer there wor a wa' andy an' Ah remember there bein' nobody left o' thad chara' except Owd Ned. T'rest on us wor aw eawtside, lined up ageean t'wa', like ducks in a shootin' gallery; an' Ah'll tell thi summat lad…bi gow id wor a cowd neet. Ah remember thinkin' Ah wouldn'd like ta be o'Pendle Hill wi nowt on bud a tripe garter…talk abeawt brass monkeys…

The Last Encounter

We stood and talked together, he and I,
Of memories fond, and friends from days gone by.
We smiled and laughed and gaily reminisced;
But mentioned not our love, nor how we'd kissed
Together in those days so long ago
And lain together as we watched the slow
White, snow-white clouds traverse the summer sky;
When we were young together, he and I.

Last time we met we did not touch or kiss,
Not even though we surely knew that this
Chance meeting never could occur again;
Nor words be said, to wipe away the pain
We both had felt throughout the passing years;
In loveless lives with loneliness and tears.
Our eyes, though fading, often met that day,
But hearts were hidden deep and kept at bay.

Then having talked, we gaily said goodbye,
To live our empty lives out, he and I.
Once I looked back, but as before he'd gone;
My joy, my youth, again I was alone.
Tonight my paper swims before my eyes,
He is not dead, how can they print such lies,
The love we bore each other cannot die,
We'll meet again, I know it, he and I.

The Old Man

He sat beneath the beeches in the park,
And fed the ducks and watched the children play,
He often came, and stayed until the dark
Shadows of evening folded on the day.

But sometimes, sitting there, he scarcely heard
The gentle birdsong, or the shouts of joy,
As triggered off by some half-shouted word,
Shot through the years the image of a boy.

His boy, enfolded in his Rachel's arms:
And then the old man's face would cloud with pain,
Recalling cruel klaxons' shrill alarms,
Smashed doors, storm troopers, terror on a train.

Those awful trains. The misery, the stench.
Arriving they'd no time to say goodbye.
Next day he saw them lying in a trench,
Piteous wrecks. If only he could die.

But he had lived. Had suffered, but survived,
Had won his freedom, and outlived his fears
Yet still a word, a look, contrived
To break his heart and flood his eyes with tears.

Pathetic now he seems to passers-by,
Yet once he'd loved and been as one of these
Who laughed and played beneath a summer sky;
The old man, on a bench beneath the trees.

Hold My Hand

"Come along dear, hold my hand," Miss Meredith said, seeing the desolation behind the immensity of the child's wide blue eyes. With a pang she remembered all the years and all the children who had responded with a trusting hand.

Through all those years the rewarding look of acceptance and complete faith which now shone in the child's grimy, tearstained, upturned face never failed to tear her inward composure; such love had sustained her and helped to compensate for the loneliness of her bedsitter and the chastity of her bed.

She had thought when she was thirty, that when she retired and no more had to present an image of virtue and good example, that she would buy a cottage in the country, where she could read her books and potter in a garden brimming with hollyhocks and roses.

But as the years sped by her savings diminished: becoming inadequate, not through personal extravagance, but due more to inflation and christening presents and engagement presents and wedding presents and birthday presents for other people's children.

Her childhood friends and college friends had all married or were dead. She felt like an interloper or some kind of freak in the presence of many of her relatives and shied from their company especially those who organised dinner parties in order to introduce her to some man "who would make you the perfect husband." Though these charades had dwindled in number as she grew older they were replaced not by acceptance of her preferred maidenly status, but by a kind of irritated assumption that she was odd, a lost cause to whom it was no longer necessary to be more than barely polite.

It was only to herself that she admitted that her preference was simply due to the fact that she had never met a man who could share her enthusiasm for the beauties of nature which stirred her to such passions of delight. She had never been able to confide in anyone the pleasure she felt when she looked out at the purity of snow, or up at the perfection of trees, nor could she find words to describe the wild stirrings she felt when walking across moors in a storm, when the steel, cold rain hurt her face and cleansed her soul.

Once or twice her parents had phoned her from the South. "Come and stay with us and have a nice rest." So she had gone and endured their desultory conversation. She had tried to introduce them to concerts and art; she had taken them to beautiful old buildings, but she could not bear the passive way with which they looked and said "How nice." It made her full of anger and hatred and remorse for the two devoted people who had created and educated her.

She was fifty when her father died and wept bitterly at his funeral, not for his death, but for all the love she might have given him, instead of care and duty.

After his death she went to Rome. Not as a pilgrim to the Holy City but as a worshipper of beauty and antiquity. She returned refreshed in spirit, replete. At last, here was fulfilment.

The following year she visited Spain. Not the overdeveloped jungle of the ravaged coastline, but the old cities and towns were history oozed from the warm stones, and the sun-dappled splendour of the Alhambra filled her heart to bursting.

The next year she decided to visit Egypt, but that year Aunty Ida became ill and she could not refuse the pleas of relatives to give her a home because she was the only one without ties.

She cared for the irascible, ailing, old lady for six years, and had not felt bitter when the will was read to find that she had been left a tenth share like the sisters who had closed their doors to their benefactress.

She felt no malice but rejoiced in her freedom which was now to be total, as today she was retiring. Suddenly the thought became a tight band round her throat, creating panic, fear, or what…?

"Please Miss", the little hand tugged her back to reality. She looked down, how many children…was it really forty years since a bright-eyed girl had stood with trepidation before a class of five-year olds…

"Yes dear" she said, "what is it,"…for the last time.

Next day she went along to the travel agents, determined to continue her travels.

She went to Holland and paid tribute to Rembrandt, then, feeling frivolous, took a barge trip on the canal, visited the tulip fields and along with the other tourists bought some chunky, cheap pottery in dubious taste. Suddenly she felt free. It no longer mattered that everything must have a lasting value and purpose. At the most she might only have ten or fifteen years of active life left and she was going to enjoy them to the full. She became the life and soul of the party and could hardly believe that she had ever been lonely.

Returning from a trip one day, a presentable, well-dressed man of her own age sat beside her, they talked and laughed and discovered many mutual likes and dislikes.

Back at the hotel he asked if she would join him for a drink before dinner, she agreed and during their conversation she told him of her plans to visit other European capitals and they found their plans to be identical. She found too that, like he, he had never married, as the public school where he had taught for forty years had provided living quarters for bachelors only,

"And I was too lazy to move," He jested.

They sat together at dinner and lingered over coffee and liqueurs. They parted on the second floor where he had his room and she continued to her own on the fourth.

It was as she rounded the bend of the staircase to the fourth floor that she suddenly felt dizzy. She smiled to herself. Excitement, high-living and too much wine at dinner she thought...

When she woke in the hospital bed she wondered what the blurred ceiling was. She remembered nothing of Holland but thought that she could hear her father's voice. She tried to move but could not make her body respond. She tried to speak but her mouth would not move. A man whose face seemed quite strange hovered somewhere above her. It was not her father but she could still hear his voice in the background. She thought she heard him tell her to stroke something, but the voice was a long way off. She tried desperately to stroke whatever it was that he wanted her to touch, but her hand was no longer hers to command.

Slowly it seemed to her that she was going to cry.

Oh Daddy, where was he? Why was he talking to her from so far away, and why was the strange man looking down at her and crying? She could bear it no longer, tears flowed down one side of her face, the other side hung limply.

When the tears cleared the man's face had disappeared and her father had stopped talking; instead a young woman with a pink face was looking down at her.

"Come along dear" the nurse said kindly, seeing the desolation in the woman's faded blue eyes. "Let me hold your hand until you go to sleep."

The Gardener

He stands amongst the potted plants,
The rusty tools, twine, shards and seeds,
Here in the crumbling garden shed,
This is his world, here are his needs.
Here he is king, a man again,
Here are decisions he can make,
His thoughts and actions are his own,
All efforts now for pleasure's sake.
In solitude he heals his soul,
Here in the cool and in the heat,
Tending the shoots with gentle care,
Shuffling around on silent feet.
His gardening clothes are old and worn,
The pockets stretched, the elbows holed,
The trousers tied around with string
Engulf his feet, fold upon fold.
His finger joints, enlarged and gnarled,
Bear witness to the passing years;
Sunk deep in wrinkled, parchment face,
The rheumy eyes, now prone to tears,
Peer dimly at the miracles
That thrust to life, row after row;
Gone are the cares of world and wife,
His movements like his heartbeats, slow.
Slow is the pain that dully stirs,
Quick the response of sudden fear.
Beneath his hands the workbench blurs,
He knows at last his end is near.
The sunbeams through the dusty panes
Light spiders hung on dusty webs
And coax to life the dormant seeds,
Whilst on the floor a man's life ebbs.
His wife calls from her kitchen clean;
His old dog wanders through the door,
It smells his hand and licks his face
Then lies beside him on the floor.
A curious beetle skirts his head,
Then darts off at the sudden sound
Of rain, that cools the sultry air
And beats the roses to the ground.
Frail blooms for which he'd lived his life,
Sought their perfection, now blood red
Eddying, the petals float,
In rivulets past the garden shed.

T' Top Shop

When Ah wor little thur wer seldom a day
Thad wi didn'd go to t'top shop,
Fer a bar o'sooap, a quarthren o' tay,
A bun or a bottle o' pop.

Bud neawadays Ah seldom set foot through t'dooar;
Fer one thing Ah carned ged up broo:
Tha sees, mi rheumatics mek mi knees sooar,
An' neaw Ah've geet bronchitis too.

Last time Ah went theer Ah felt reyt eawt o'place,
Tho' t'fellah wer ever so nice, Tha sees,
Ah felt daft, 'cos Ah'd th'ony white face,
An' t'shop, well, id fair stunk o' spice.

Neaw when Ah wor a lass t'smells wer gradely theer,
Warm bread, an' lamp oil an' coffee;
An' t'windas warn'd filled up wi' fags an' wi' beer,
Bud row afther row o' toffee.

T'shopkeeper then wor a little owd woman,
Wi grey 'air done up in a bun,
Eccentric an' lonely, ruled o'er bi no mon,
Some thowt 'er a figure o' fun.

Some kids off t'street 'ud run in an' torment 'er
An' ask if oo'd geet an iced bun,
Then they'd aw sheawt- "Goo an' skate on id" to 'er,
An' think id a reyt bit o' fun.

Or else 'avin' asked fer Wild Woodbines they'd sheawt,
"Well why doesn'd ta tame 'em then".
Then gigglin' an' laughin' they'd rush to ged eawt,
As if t'shop wor a lions' den.

Bud 'er greawnd be'ind counter Miss 'Indle stood,
An' calmly took aw thi' could give,
Sellin' donkey stooans, vinegar an' firewood,
Aw t' little things needed to live.

'Er money warn'd kept in a big shiny till,
Bud i' tins scattered aw reawnd t'shop,
Ah con see 'er reychin' fer t' Minto tin yet,
An' 'ear t' noise o't' theepenny bits drop.

Fooaks rumoured Miss 'Indle wor not short o' brass
Until one windy September day,
Sweepin' t' leaves off 'er flags, oo wor killed, poor lass,
Wi' a 'orse an' cart runaway.

'Er body wor picked up an' teken inside
Bi Fred, one o't' local carters;
'E sed t' gossips as cawd 'er weel off 'ad lied
'Cos oo on'y wore rag garters!

A part o't' street deed when Miss 'Indle wer killed,
Id never wer quite same agen,
An' tho' t'shop's bin painted an' aw t'shelves are filled,
It's lost t'magic as id 'ed then.

It's nod thad Ah've owt ageean coloured fooak
There's some thad is kind as con be,
It's not just thad Ah carned untherstand their talk,
But they dunna untherstand me.

Neaw, Ah dorn'd goo up to t' top shop ony mooar,
Mi 'ome 'elp brings me aw Ah eyt.
An' while t'milk chap 'ull 'ev a gossip at t'dooar
Why bless their kind 'earts, Ah'm aw reyt.

T'Music O'Life

It's Sunda' neet, an' Ah'm sittin' i't'charch
Listenin' ta t'th'organ play,
Id music ne'er fails ta warm mi owd 'eart,
Even o't'cowdest day.

An' as Ah sit 'ere mi mind's floatin' back,
Back to a summer's day,
When th'organ wor playin' us weddin' march,
An' wi wor young an' gay.

Wi went ta Blackpoo' fer us 'oneymoon,
An' danced i't'Teawr aw neet,
By gum! my Bill wor an' 'ansome lad then,
An' nimble on 'is feet.

An' when Reg o'th'organ 'ad played t'last waltz
Wi walked back under t'stars,
An' music followed us aw t'way 'ooam
Fro't'pier an't'corner bars.

When wi geet us fost 'eawse wi bowt us'sel'
A little gramophone,
An' we'd records o' Gracie an' Formby,
An' one of 'Ome Sweet 'Ome.

Wi wor booath i't'choir, Bill an' me,
An' booath luv'd ta sing
Hymns an' carols, 'n 'Andel's Messiah
Or onny bloomin' thing!

O' Sunda's wi used ta walk inta t'park
An' listen ta t'brass band;
Sometimes t'Salvation Army wor theer,
An' t'noise they med wor grand.

Bud then, i't'September o'thirty-nine,
T'music o'life stood still,
An' young men i'luv wi luv an' wi life
Like Bill, wor thrained ta kill.

Six long years passed afoor Bill an' me
Could caw us lives us own,
An' t'babbies Ah'd sung ta sleep o'mi knee
Ta sthrappin' lads 'ad grown.

Tho' Ah feawnd no time fer t'choir practice
While t'lads wor growin' up,
My Bill wor a member o't'male voice choir,
An' twice they won a cup!

Las' year t'lads bowt us a record player,
A reight posh thing an' aw,
Bud wi carned put blessed thing on at full
Id blasts us through th'eawse wa'!

Nay - thad noise thi call music neawadays
Does nowt fer Bill ner me.
Ah'm a silly owd foo' ta talk like thad
'Cos neaw, there's on'y me.

A week la' Frida' eawr Lord took my Bill,
That's why Ah'm sittin' 'ere
Listenin' ta th'organ, an' picturin' 'im
Standin' at th'altar theer,

Fer tho' Ah carn'd ever touch 'im ageean,
Until mi deein' day
Ah'll see 'is warm smile, an' 'ear is kind voice
When Ah 'ear music play.

Movin' Day

Oo set i't'middle o't'kitchin flooar
O't th' on'y seat oo could find,
Waitin' fer t'van ta come to 'er dooar,
Tho' t'van wor nod on 'er mind.

'Er owd 'eyd wor swimmin' wi' memories
Of 'appier days long gone,
An' clear in 'er thowts an 'er memories
Wor aw 'er childer an' John.

Oo rembered t'day they'd getten wed;
They wor booath just eighteen.
Aw thi'ed then wor a table an' bed,
An' a tay-chest painted green.

Bud their 'earts wor bustin' wi' love an' 'ope,
Feelin's thad lasted thro' years;
A love that'd 'elped 'em booath ta cope
An' sweetened aw their tears.

Tho' seven bonny childer 'ad kept 'em poor,
They 'ad allus paid their way,
Till death 'ad come knockin' ad their dooar
An' Jack wor tekken away.

Fer when 'e deed oo wor aw alooan,
'Cos t'childer aw lived away;
Bud as oo'd never bin one ta mooan
Oo'd smiled an' oo'd nod gi'n way.

Oo'd carried on thryin' ta mek a do,
Cuttin' deawn on aw oo could,
Bud t' bills kept on comin', an' t'worries grew
An' 'er 'eart wor nod sa good.

An' then one cowd day a letter 'ad come.
They wor pullin' th' 'eawses down.
Thi sed oo could 'ev a new little flat
In another part o't'teawn.

Thur warn't mony things oo wanted ta pack,
They aw seemed shabby some 'eaw;
Some photos o't'lads an one of 'er Jack
Wor aw thad oo wanted neaw.

Oo sthrooaked 'em gently an' kissed 'em aw
As if they wor flesh an' blood;
Oo looked at t'cleyn marks as they'd left o't'wa'
An' knew they'd aw gone fer good.

Id wor all o'er neaw, oo shut 'er owd eyes,
Oo didn'd want na mooar,
Oo deed i't'cheear, oo'd sed 'er goodbyes
When t'van pulled up at t'dooar.

Return of the Native

Last night I wept for my home town, for simple pleasures lost.
Do men, uncaring for the past think what the future's cost.
I had returned to see once more the scenes of carefree youth,
Now memories of golden days lie tarnished by cold truth.
The paths we trod, the tiny lanes, the hawthorn blossoms sweet,
The hedgerows and the brown trout stream lie 'neath a cold grey street.
A block of flats now stands forlorn where happy children lay
On warm green banks to fish in streams clear as a summer's day:
The small dark pools. the sunlit shallows culverted away,
Their silver fish and waving weeds denied the light of day.
The slanting sun of evening now glistens on concrete walls.
Gone are the songs of nightingales as darkness slowly falls,
For starling flocks have taken o'er, they crowd the ledges high,
And cornices of civic pride beneath their thick lime lie.
The park where lovers met and walked in silence bleak now lies,
Whilst from bedraggled flower beds crumbling moss-grown statues rise.
And daubed with paint and obscene words a broken wood bench sags
Amidst a sea of rusting cans and pulpy plastic bags.
My memories still hold for me the gleam of sun on brass,
Of bandsmen red and blue and gold, of children on the grass.
How quickly time destroys our dreams, our fleeting pleasures past,
And Man, the ruler of the world, is loser at the last.